TAKE FIVE

THIS BOOK BELONGS TO

TAKE FIVE

NIALL BRESLIN

ILLUSTRATED BY SHEENA DEMPSEY

GILL BOOKS

Gill Books
Hume Avenue
Park West
Dublin 12
www.gillbooks.ie

Gill Books is an imprint of M.H. Gill and Co.

Text © Niall Breslin 2019
Illustrations © Sheena Dempsey 2019
978 07171 8553 5

Designed by www.grahamthew.com
Printed by LEGO SpA, Italy

A NOTE FOR PARENTS

The world is changing, and it's changing fast. We do our best to try and keep up with its ever-increasing pace, but sometimes we just can't. We all feel this from time to time, including our kids.

When we do have time to be around the people we love, our minds are often pulled away to the future or stuck reliving the past. This world constantly demands our attention, so quite often we can't offer our presence to the things and people who truly matter. Giving someone your true presence in today's society is quite simply the greatest gift you can offer. But it's hard. There are so many commands on our energy. This always-on, always-contactable, always-available culture is limiting our ability to be mindful and to be aware of those around us – how we influence others and how they influence us.

This isn't sustainable anymore. Ironically, through our constant desire to get somewhere, we actually miss living. The good stuff exists right in front of us, right now.

Having not seen my nephew for a while, I recently popped over for a visit. I got out of the car and he ran out to the garden to embrace me. These are my favourite moments – the ones that linger far after they happen. But I was too busy on my phone talking about something that really didn't matter, so I missed that moment with him.

You see, we are relentlessly exposed to picture-perfect lives and highlight reels, so we tend to focus an unbalanced level of energy on the stuff we don't have rather than the stuff we do have. If you are like me, you may find yourself passing self-judgement about the fact that you don't have the same type of life as some random person online whom you will never meet. We need to try and learn how to value what's right in front of us. This is where those perfect moments lie, not with our faces in our phones wondering what it would be like to be someone else. You are yourself.

Our kids see and feel this, and it's only natural for them to crave it, too. We are all attached to having lovely experiences and nice things, but the reality is we can't always have them. Life is not a straight line.

That is why developing a practice of gratitude at an early age can really support a kid's ability to recognise that they may not need all these things, and that they can't always have only pleasant experiences. It's important for their emotional development to understand that, but it's also important that they have a role model who shows this.

For parents and kids alike, gratitude is a brilliant trait to bring into your daily routine. Positive psychology and neuroscience evidence highlights this, and it's a core construct of effective mindfulness practice.

I am very thankful for the opportunity to write this book for kids. They are our future in an uncertain world and we need to do our best to help provide them with the tools to navigate it.

Bressie

It was Saturday and Freddie was very excited.
He was going to his best friend Ben's birthday party.
Ben lived on his road and had the best parties ever.

Freddie helped his mum wrap Ben's present, being careful not to tear the wrapping paper. He couldn't wait to give Ben the walkie-talkie set. He knew Ben was going to love it.

'Guess what, Mum? Ben is having a bouncy castle at his party!'

'Oh wow,' said Mum. 'You'll have so much fun bouncing on it with all your friends.'

'Can I have a bouncy castle for my birthday party, Mum?'

'We'll see, Freddie.'

'Don't forget Nana is collecting you later,' said Mum.

'Hurray,' cheered Freddie. 'I can't wait to see Nana! This is going to be a great day.'

'Happy birthday, Ben,' said Freddie, handing him
his present and the card he had made.

'Thank you,' said Ben, putting Freddie's carefully wrapped
present on top of a big pile of gifts.

'I got you a walkie-talkie set. Want to open it now so
we can play?' asked Freddie.

'Not yet,' said Ben. 'Come and see what I have in the garden.'

Outside there were lots of children running around, playing games with balloons, jumping on the bouncy castle and making noise with party horns.

'Look, Freddie, look – there it is!' shouted Ben.

Freddie couldn't believe his eyes. There, right in front of him, was the coolest go kart he had ever seen.

'Wow, it's so cool. Can I have a go?' he asked.

'You can have a turn another day,' said Ben. 'I'm the only one who can go on it today because it's my birthday.'

All of a sudden, Freddie got a strange feeling in his chest.

He thought that Ben was being a bit mean. He only wanted
a quick turn of the go kart.

Freddie was a little bit quiet for the rest of the party.
He didn't feel like eating cake or playing any
of the party games.

He just wanted to go home, but he
knew he had to wait for Nana
to pick him up.

Finally, Nana arrived. Just as Freddie was getting ready to go Ben handed him one of the walkie-talkies.

'They actually work,' said Ben. 'Brontosaurus Ben to T-Rex Freddie. Do. You. Read. Me?'

'I don't want to play,' said Freddie. 'I just want to go home.'

On the way home, Nana noticed that Freddie wasn't himself.

'Did you have fun?' she asked gently.

Freddie nodded.

'Why didn't you want to try the walkie-talkie set with Ben?'

Anna's

OPEN!

'It's just that Ben wouldn't
let me have a turn on his go kart, and
I'm supposed to be his best friend.'

'Oh, I see,' said Nana. 'I think we need
to Take Five.'

Nana took Freddie the long way home, through the park.

'Do you wish you had a go kart just like Ben, Freddie?'

'Yes.'

'I feel the same sometimes,' said Nana.

'You want a go kart, too?'

Nana laughed.

'No, Freddie. But there are lots of times I want something
I don't have. Like the time my neighbour Emma got a
convertible car, I was so jealous! I didn't want my boring
old red car with a roof anymore, I wanted a shiny black one
with no roof like hers.'

'But do you know what I do when I feel sad or upset about not having something I want?'

Freddie leaned forward curiously.

'What, Nana?'

'I just Take Five. I think of things that make life fun and count each finger one by one.'

'Take one hand and grab the thumb on your other hand,' said Nana.

Freddie grabbed his thumb.

'This is number one. Take a deep breath and think about something in your life that makes you happy.'

Freddie thought about his dog Larry and how he couldn't wait to get home to play with him.

'Now grab the finger beside your thumb. This is number two,' said Nana. 'Think of another thing you have.'

Freddie thought about his friends and how much he likes playing with them in the yard at school.

'Good! Now take your middle finger. This is number three.'

Freddie took a deep breath and looked around him.

'I love this park!' he shouted.

'You're getting the hang of this,' said Nana.

With a big smile on his face, Freddie moved to his fourth finger, looking down at the cool new runners his mum had bought him.

Then, grabbing his little finger, Freddie took one last deep
breath and thought of how happy it makes him when Nana
comes to visit or picks him up from school. He thought of
the warm feeling he gets in his tummy when Nana gives
him one of her world-famous Nana hugs and how she
always makes everything better.

As they arrived home, Freddie gave Nana a great big hug.

'Nana, you are my baby finger.'

'Freddie, you are my baby finger, too.'

Later that afternoon, Freddie realised that Nana's trick had worked! He was feeling so happy about all of the nice things in his life that he forgot about the things he didn't have. Then he remembered the walkie-talkie in his pocket.

'Come in, Brontosaurus Ben. This is T-Rex Freddie. Do. You. Want. To. Play?'

'This is Brontosaurus Ben. Yes! Meet. You. In. The. Garden.'

Having a friend like Ben was another thing Freddie was grateful for. That's six. He was going to have to move on to his other hand!

The Take Five trick is a really great way to remember
all the things you're grateful for. I do this trick every day.
Why don't you give it a try?

THINK OF THINGS THAT MAKE LIFE FUN
AND COUNT EACH FINGER ONE BY ONE!

1. ....

2. ....

3. ....

4. ....

5. ....